The WINNERS

LET'S PUT THE EQUIPMENT FOR OUR LATEST CONTEST INTO THE CAR!

WE'LL BRING OUT THE REST OF IT, DAD!

SLEDGEHAMMERS?

WHAT KIND OF CONTEST DO THEY NEED THOSE THINGS FOR?

I KNOW - THEY MUST BE ENTERING A PIANO SMASHING CONTEST!

I'LL HAVE A GO MYSELF - I'M MUCH STRONGER THAN THAT PUNY LOT!

GULP! EVEN I CAN'T SPIN A SLEDGEHAMMER LIKE THAT! THEY MUST HAVE A 'TECHNIQUE' FOR SMASHING PIANOS!

TWIRL!

I'LL BEAT THEM YET . . . I'LL JUST HAVE TO DO . . . SOME EXTRA TRAINING FIRST! PUFF!

PUFF! GASP!

SO . . .

LET'S GO WIN THAT CONTEST, FAMILY!

DON'T COUNT ON IT! HEH, HEH!

WOW! THIS MUST BE A POSH PIANO SMASHING CONTEST!

SNOOTY MANOR

OH, NO - IT'S CROQUET!

THAT'S RIGHT - AND AS USUAL, WE'RE 'HAMMERING' THE OPPOSITION!

BOK!

ROBOPLOD

COPPER OF THE FUTURE

ROBOPLOD! ALL THESE £1,000 NOTES WE GOT IN OUR POCKET-MONEY ARE *FORGERIES!* WE CAN'T SPEND THEM!

GIVE ME A COUPLE OF THE FAKE NOTES, KIDS! I SHALL ANALYSE THE PRINTING INK IN MY *LABORATUMMY!*

CHOMP!

GULP! BURP! GOOD!.. THE PRINTING INK HAS BEEN IDENTIFIED!

PEEP! BURP! DING!

NOW MY SUPER-SENSITIVE LONG-NOSE-OF-THE-LAW WILL TRACK DOWN THE INK TO THE FORGER'S DEN!

PEEP! PEEP!

GLEE! FIFTEEN BILLION POUNDS... I SHALL FLOOD THE POCKET-MONEY MARKET WITH FORGERIES!

FORWARD ▶ ◀ REVERSE

SNIP!

I'VE FOUND THE FORGER'S DEN...

CORONATION PROGRAMME PRINTERS

I'LL MAKE A SLIGHT READJUSTMENT TO THE PRINTING PRESS!

TUG!

RWARD ◀REVERSE

AAARGH! WHAT'S GONE WRONG? COME BACK!

COME HERE, MY FLEXIBLE FRIEND!

YOU KIDS CAN SHARE THE REWARD MONEY—AND THIS TIME IT WON'T BE FAKE!

PUSH!

HOORAY!

B.Glennard.

ERK! IT'S... **TOM THUG** THE BRAINLESS BULLY!

I HEAR YOU'VE BEEN BULLYING THE OTHER CHILDREN AGAIN, TOM!

WHO? *ME?* NAHH... WOULDN'T *DREAM* OF IT!

GRR! I *KNOW* TOM'S GUILTY, BUT I CAN'T *PROVE* IT!

LEAVE IT TO ME!

NEXT DAY... COR! I'VE BEEN INVITED TO A *BULLIES CONVENTION* AT THE TOWN 'ALL!

LATER... BRILL! I FEEL RIGHT AT 'OME 'ERE!

ANNUAL BULLIES CONVENTIO

YEAH, I RECKON I'VE CAUSED MORE AGGRO THIS YEAR THAN ANYONE!

HAH!

I'M THE BEST BULLY 'ERE!

TELL US ABOUT IT!

WELL, I PINCH DINNER MONEY FROM LITTLE KIDS... COPY ANSWERS IN CLASS... THREATEN WIMPS TO DO ME 'OMEWORK...

VERY INTERESTING...

...AND JUST THE SORT OF CONFESSION WE NEEDED!

AWK! THEY'RE ALL *TEACHERS* IN DISGUISE!

THE PLAN WORKED!

SPIN!

BAH! THAT CONVENTION TURNED INTO A *CONFESSIONAL!* WOT A *CON!*

HISTORY
MATHS
ENGLISH
MORE MATHS
SCIENCE

LEW STRINGER

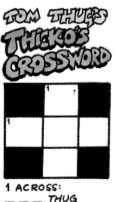

TOM THUG'S Thicko's CROSSWORD

1 ACROSS:
___ THUG
DOWN:
UH... SAME AS 1 ACROSS

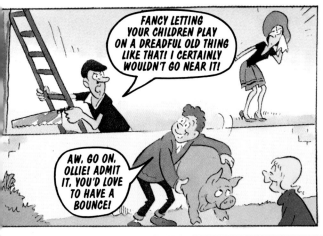

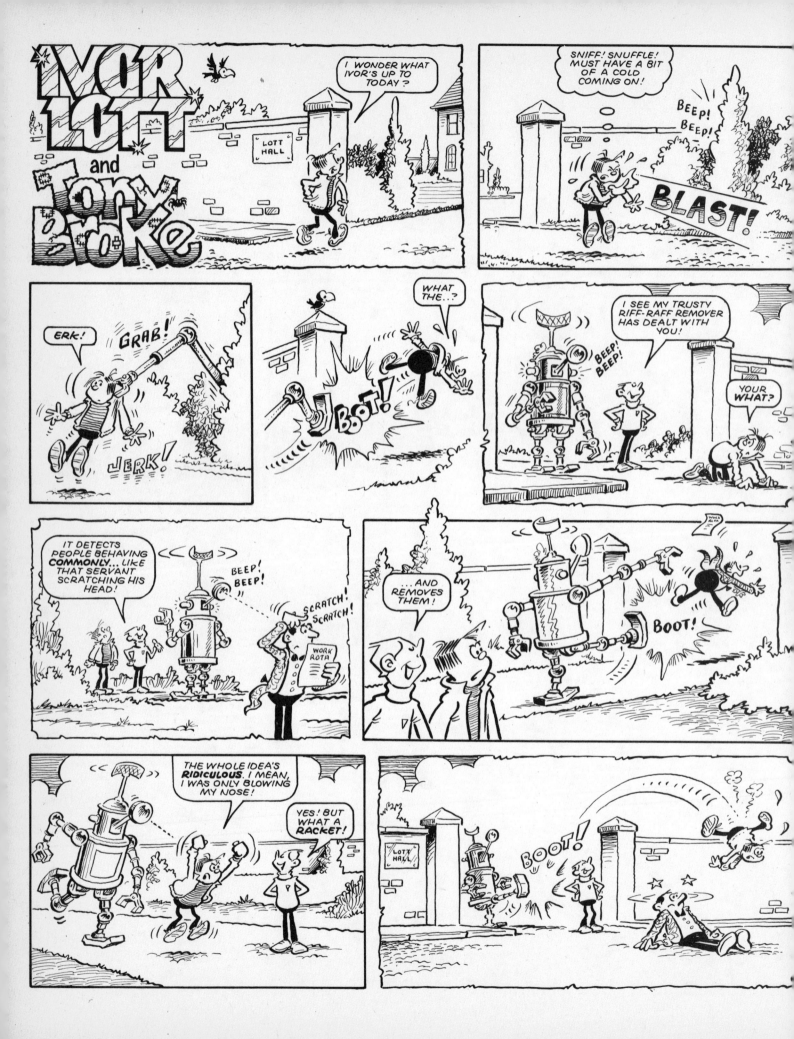

Jack Pott

The Scruffs... TOP of the CLASS teach ...The Toffs

PETE'S POP-UP BOOK

BAH! MY BOILED EGG'S ALL SQUELCHY! MUM NEVER MAKES IT HARD ENOUGH!

CRACK! SPLOSH!

I'LL GET A PROPER HARD-BOILED EGG FROM MY POP-UP BOOK!

BUT...

HELLO! HUMPTY-DUMPTY'S THE NAME — FALLING OFF WALLS IS MY GAME! HEH, HEH!

GROAN!

WHAT'S THIS? YOU'VE SMASHED ONE OF MY MATES, YOU THUG!

B-BUT..!

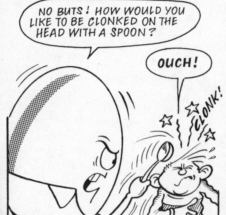

NO BUTS! HOW WOULD YOU LIKE TO BE CLONKED ON THE HEAD WITH A SPOON?

OUCH!

CLONK!

CHUCKLE! HAVING TROUBLE WITH YOUR EGG, FROM YOUR BOOK, PETE?

STOP! THIS IS NO **YOLKING** MATTER!

BUT...

YOUR MUM'S JUST AS BAD! ALWAYS GETTING MY MATES INTO **HOT WATER**!

EEK!

WHERE DID THEY GO?

N-NO, HUMPTY! DON'T CLIMB ON THAT WALL!

TERRY BAVE

AAAGGHH!

TOO LATE!

WE'LL HAVE TO PUT HIM BACK TOGETHER AGAIN, PETE!

BUT...

BAH! YOU'RE NO BETTER THAN ALL THE KING'S HORSES, AND ALL THE KING'S MEN!

THE DUMMIES

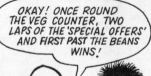

The WINNERS

AT THE BOXING STADIUM...

TO THE DRESSING ROOMS

I'M POSITIVE BATTLING BONZO FROM BATTERSEA IS GOING TO WIN TONIGHT!

BUT...

BONZO'S LOST HIS CONFIDENCE! GO IN THERE AND CHEER HIM UP!

LEAVE IT TO US!

HELLO, BONZO! WE'RE THE WINNERS!

AND YOU CAN'T LOSE TONIGHT 'COS WE'RE ON YOUR SIDE!

THAT'S RIGHT... AND WE NEVER LOSE!

IS THAT SO?

JAB!

DODGE!

GREAT! I FEEL A LOT BETTER NOW! JUST LET ME OUT THERE — I'LL SPIFFLICATE HIM!

JAB!

OH-OH! MIND THAT...

DODGE!

...TOO LATE!

BAH! LOOK WHAT YOU'VE DONE!...HE'S OUT COLD...AND HE'S NOT EVEN IN THE RING YET!

SORRY!

LISTEN TO THAT! IF I TELL 'EM THE FIGHT'S OFF THERE'LL BE A RIOT! YOU'LL HAVE TO STAND-IN FOR HIM!

WHY ARE WE ♪ WAITING...?

SO...

GULP! B-BUT HE'LL S-SPIFFLICATE ME!

SO WILL THIS LOT IF YOU BACK OUT NOW!

LATER...

GROAN! I LOST! HE GAVE ME A RIGHT PASTING!

DON'T WORRY, DEAR—SOME GOOD CAME OUT OF IT!

WE COLLECTED A FORTUNE ON YOUR INSURANCE POLICY!

OUR NEW HISTORY TEACHER HASN'T ARRIVED!

THAT'S GREAT - WE CAN HAVE A GAME OF 'IT'!

UH-OH! HERE HE COMES - I'D BETTER WARN THE OTHERS!

BUT . . .

TOO LATE!

OOPS!

OUCH!

GRRR! YOU CAN ALL TAKE 500 LINES!

MEANWHILE, YOU CAN CARRY MY THINGS INTO THE CLASSROOM!

PUFF! WHAT A WEIGHT!

NO WONDER THEY'RE HEAVY . . . THE BOXES ARE FULL OF TOOLS!

THAT'S RIGHT! MY HOBBY IS ARCHAEOLOGY!

AND RAY'S SPECIAL SPECS WILL HELP ME FIND THINGS TO DIG UP!

JUST LET ME KNOW WHEN YOU SPOT SOMETHING, RAY!

GASP!

I TAKE IT YOU'D BE INTERESTED IN OLD BONES, SIR!

YOU BET!

WELL THIS GARDEN'S FULL OF THEM!

COME ON - WHAT ARE WE WAITING FOR?

HOW OLD DO YOU RECKON THESE BONES ARE, RAY?

NOT VERY OLD, SIR - "FANG" HERE BURIED THEM ONLY LAST WEEK!

GRRR!

NOW WE CAN GET BACK TO OUR GAME! AFTER ALL, TEACHER IS PLAYING 'IT' WITH FANG!

FACEACHE

WE'VE GOT AN ART CLASS DETENTION FOR SPILLING PAINT . . . AND IT WASN'T EVEN OUR FAULT! GROAN!

I'LL GET US OUT OF IT!

ART ROOM

YOU WON'T GO HOME 'TIL YOU'VE FINISHED DRAWING THIS STILL LIFE ARRANGEMENT!

COULDN'T WE DO A PORTRAIT INSTEAD? I'LL MODEL!

VERY SHORTLY . . .

WE'VE FINISHED, SIR!

WHAT? THEY'VE ONLY BEEN DRAWING FIVE MINUTES!

B-BUT THERE'S NO FACE! YOU HAVEN'T DRAWN ANY FEATURES!

WE'VE JUST DRAWN WHAT WE CAN SEE, SIR!

AAGH! G-GO HOME!

BLANK SCRUNGE!

ART ROOM

HEE, HEE! YOU WERE BRILL, FACEACHE!

OH, IT WAS NOTHING! GIGGLE!

Melvyn's Mirror

The VAMPIRE BRATS

GREAT NEWS! A PAIR OF RARE FISH-EAGLES HAVE NESTED IN ONE OF THOSE TALL TREES...WE'RE OFF TO SEE IF ANY EGGS HAVE BEEN LAID YET!

EEK! LOOK, BROTHER BRAT! BET HE'S A SNEAKY, RARE-EGG COLLECTOR, CLIMBING THAT TREE TO PINCH THE FISH-EAGLE'S EGGS!

SORRY TO DISTURB YOU, MRS FISH-EAGLE...BUT A SNEAKY RARE-EGG THIEF IS CLIMBING UP TO ROB YOU OF YOUR EGGS!

NOT TO WORRY, THOUGH — WE'LL MOVE YOU AND YOUR NEST TO THE NEXT TREE! LIFT, BROTHER BRAT!

YOU'LL BE SAFE HERE! NOW...WE'LL FLY BACK TO YOUR OLD TREE AND...

...WAIT FOR THE EGG THIEF!

PUFF! GLEE! NEARLY THERE! I'LL SOON HAVE THOSE EGGS IN MY BAG! PUFF!

FLAP! FLAP! FLAP!

AAARGH! I'M OFF! I'LL GO BACK TO COLLECTING CAR NUMBERS!

SHOOOM!

HO-HO-HO! BET HE'LL NEVER PINCH ANOTHER EGG AGAIN!

OOF! UGH! OI! YOUR MATE'S IN THAT TREE!

THANK GOODNESS! I'D HATE MY KIDS TO HATCH OUT LOOKING LIKE THESE TWO!

The Scruffs... **TOP of the CLASS** ...The Toffs

WONDER WELLIES

NASTY NORMAN

FRIGHT School

MUMMY'S BOY

It's a Nice Life

FACEACHE
the boy with a THOUSAND FACES!

COO! THAT'S THE BEST FILM I'VE SEEN FOR AGES, FACEACHE!

THE UGLY CREEPY THING FROM THE SWAMP

THE END

OUTSIDE...

ALL THIS WEEK THE UGLY CREEPY THING FROM THE SWAMP

OI, KID! WHAT'S THE FILM LIKE? IS IT WORTH WATCHING?

WORTH WATCHING? I'LL SAY! IT'S ABSOLUTELY ACE! MEGA-FANTASTIC!

HMM! THIS COULD BE GOOD FOR BUSINESS!

MANAGER

IT'S ALL ABOUT THIS HIDEOUS CREATURE THAT CRAWLS OUT OF A SWAMP...

SCRUNGE!

BLEARGH!

...IT GOES ON THE RAMPAGE, TERRORISING THE COUNTRY! NOTHING CAN STOP IT!

...BUT JUST THEN, THIS BIG ALIEN FROM JUPITER LANDS, HOPING TO TAKE OVER THE WORLD!

TREMBLE!

GUAKE!

SCRUNGE!

SCRUNGE!

IT ENDS UP FIGHTING THE SWAMP THING! A BITTER BATTLE RAGES... WHO WILL WIN?

SCRUNGE!

SCRUNGE!

SCRUNGE!

SCRUNGE!

STOMP!

NEITHER! THE ALIENS' RAY GUNS GO OFF ACCIDENTALLY AND THEY ZAP EACH OTHER! GREAT ENDING!

SPLIDGE

ZAPPED MONSTER SCRUNGE!

OKAY, RUN ALONG HOME, SONNY! THIS WAY FOR THE NEXT FILM PERFORMANCE!

SHOVE!

FORGET IT! THERE'S NO POINT WATCHING IT NOW THAT WEIRD KID'S TOLD US THE PLOT!

B-BUT...

WHY, YOU...YOU LITTLE MONSTER! GRAAGH!

ULP! CURLY, I THINK I'VE PUT MY FOOT...ER, FACE IN IT, AGAIN!

THE DUMMIES

SCHOOL TEAM

We're playing against some German children in the Black Forest!

We don't want to get lost, so I'll leave a trail of bread crumbs!

But...

Oh, no! Smudge and Olga are eating our trail!

Munch! Delicious!

Now we ARE lost!

Don't panic! We'll just follow our noses!

Four hours later...

Bah! Your nose must be bent, sir! That's the TENTH TIME we've passed that old tree trunk!

My nose smells food! And it's coming from over there!

Sniff!

Good old Olga!

Who are you?

Pupils from the Gasbag Road School in Wigan, mate!

We came here to play against some German children in 1923... and got lost!

Gulp!

Boo-hoo! We'll never get out of here!

Sob! She's right!

Then...

Olga! Wake up, Olga!

Eh? But we were all lost in the Black Forest!

Fat fool! That BLACK FOREST GATEAU she ate must have given her a BAD DREAM!

The WINNERS

The Scruffs... **TOP of the CLASS** ... The Toffs

TEST YOURSELF

Are you a Saver?

To find out, answer each of the questions, tick the appropriate one, then check your score, pals!

1 Monday morning, and you've been given your pocket-money. Do you...
A. Spend it all in one go in the sweet shop?
B. Only take a certain amount to school each day to make it last the week?
C. Spend some and put the rest into your piggy-bank?

2 Gran pops round and gives you a big bag of sweets. Do you...
A. Just have a couple, and put the rest away for another day?
B. Scoff the lot and take the risk of feeling sick?
C. Eat half of the sweets immediately and the rest in the evening?

3 Christmas, and one of your presents is your favourite annual. Do you...
A. Try to make each page last as long as possible?
B. Limit yourself to reading just a few pages per day?
C. Plough through the whole annual in one sitting?

4 The fair comes to town for the week. Do you...
A. Raid your piggy-bank and have a go on every ride?
B. Divide your cash in half and go to the fair twice?
C. Go round seeing which rides are the best value, and then ration yourself to a couple of goes per evening?

TURN THE PAGE TO CHECK YOUR SCORE

1. A-0, B-3, C-5; 2. A-5, B-0, C-2; 3. A-2, B-5, C-0; 4. A-0, B-3, C-5.

0-4
You never save anything! If you have any sweets, you not only eat them all, you stuff several in your mouth at once!

5-12
Average. You try hard to ration things, but you always end up trying to get an advance on next week's pocket-money!

13-20
Cor! You are a saver! You always have cash in your pocket, but don't go too far... or everyone might call you 'Scrooge'!

BLUB THE SUB

OUR TEAM'S PLAYING THIS AFTERNOON — SO I'D BETTER GET READY!

YOU'VE GOT PLENTY OF TIME, BLUB!

I HAVEN'T, SALLY! BEFORE I GET A CHANCE TO PLAY I NEED TO GET RID OF THE FOUR SUBSTITUTES IN FRONT OF ME! HEH, HEH!

LATER... I'D BEST KEEP AN EYE OPEN FOR BLUB! HE'S BOUND TO TRY AND NOBBLE ME!

*FIRST SUBSTITUTE

SPORT

SPLUDGE!

SUDDENLY... GOTCHA! ONE DOWN— THREE TO GO!

ERK!

SPORT

WATCH OUT FOR BLUB!

DON'T WORRY! HE WON'T GET US! WE'RE STICKING TOGETHER FOR SAFETY!

BUT... ROLL! AAAGGGHHH!

RUMBLE!

LOOK OUT!

THEY'RE STICKING TOGETHER NOW, ALL RIGHT! HAW, HAW!

LATER... HERE'S YOUR BIG CHANCE TO SHOW US HOW YOU CAN PLAY, BLUB! SMITH'S BEEN INJURED AND WE'VE GOT TO GET A SUB ON!

GOSH!

YIPPEEE! I DID IT! I'VE MADE THE TEAM!

AAAGGGHHH!

WHOOOSH!

16

SLIDE!

MARK BENNO.

KER-UNCH!

LUCKY FOR YOU WE MANAGED TO WIN WITH ONLY TEN MEN!

POOR BLUB! HE REALLY SLIPPED UP THAT TIME!

B-B-BLUB!

X-RAY SPECS

I COULD DO WITH A SATURDAY JOB SO I CAN EARN SOME EXTRA POCKET-MONEY!

THEN...

JOE GOODHEART — SECONDHAND CARS FOR SALE

THIS CAR'S A BARGAIN, SIR! IT HAS A LOW FUEL CONSUMPTION!

REALLY?

IT'S GOT A LOW FUEL CONSUMPTION ALL RIGHT! THE PETROL TANK'S HANGING OFF!

EH?

HEH, HEH! THIS BOY'S A BORN COMEDIAN!

OUCH!

THERE! YOU BE ON YOUR WAY NOW, SONNY!

BAH! HE'S NOT GETTING RID OF ME SO EASILY!

NOW, YOU'LL FIND THIS CAR REALLY ECONOMICAL TO RUN, SIR!

WELL, I... I DON'T KNOW...!

WHAT'S THE INSIDE OF THE ENGINE LIKE, RAY?

I'LL HAVE A LOOK!

LOW MILEAGE

ONE LADY OWNER

DEFINITELY MORE ECONOMICAL TO RUN!

THERE YOU ARE, SIR! A PERSONAL GUARANTEE FROM X-RAY SPECS HIMSELF!

FROM THE STATE OF THAT ENGINE I'D SAY IT WAS MORE ECONOMICAL FOR YOU TO RUN TO WORK AND LEAVE THE CAR AT HOME! SNIGGER!

I'LL BUY MY CAR SOMEWHERE ELSE!

GRR! THAT WAS ALL YOUR DOING!

HE GAVE ME A FIVER TO MOVE ON! I'VE FOUND MY SATURDAY JOB — ANNOYING CROOKED SECOND-HAND CAR SALESMEN!

SCHOOL BELLE

...LITTLE DOES HE KNOW THAT **TODAY** IS GOING TO BE THE MOST THRILLING DAY IN HIS SCHOOL LIFE!

HIS **BIG DAY** HAS STARTED!

COME HERE, BOY! GROTTY GLENDA AND ME **NEED** YOU!

I SAY THAT I HAVE WHITER TEETH, AND LONGER EYELASHES THAN OLD GROTTY! YOU WILL TELL HER I'M **RIGHT**!

RIGHT?

YOU WILL TELL HER SHE'S **WRONG**! RIGHT?

DIG! DIG!

OOER! I THINK I'LL PLAY **SAFE**! SO...

FLUTTER! GLEAM! GLEAM! FLUTTER!

BELLE'S TEETH GLEAM A **LITTLE** BIT MORE THAN GLENDA'S... BUT GLENDA'S EYELASHES ARE A **TEENY-WEENY** BIT LONGER THAN BELLE'S!

RIGHT, THEN... SO TELL US **WHO** HAS THE MOST LUSCIOUS, RUBY-RED, KISSY-KISSY LIPS!

THAT IS THE CLINCHER!!!

DIG! DIG!

KISS! SMOOCH! KISS! KISS! SMOOCH!

WELL, IF YOU **BOTH** KISS ME... I MIGHT BE ABLE TO TELL WHO HAS THE BEST LIPS!

I'LL PLAY SAFE AGAIN... AND TELL THEM THEY **BOTH** KISS THE **SAME**!

DOESN'T NEED TO **SAY** ANYTHING, DOES HE?? **I WIN**!

TINGLE! TINGLE! WIGGLE! WIGGLE!

FUME!

SLOWCOACH

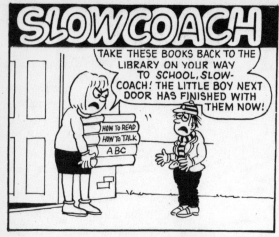

MUMMY'S BOY

Good Guy

IT'S MY TURN TO TRY TO MAKE GUY BAD TODAY! LUCKY ME — I **DON'T** THINK!

PSST! HEAR THE ONE ABOUT THE TWO SWORDSMEN WHO FOUGHT IN THE MIDDLE OF THE ROAD? IT WAS A "**DUEL**" CARRIAGEWAY!

HUH!?
CHEW! CHEW!

HO, HO! THAT WAS A GOOD ONE! I'D HAVE LAUGHED BEFORE, BUT IT'S **BAD MANNERS** WHEN YOUR MOUTH'S **FULL**!
BAH! MY BEST JOKE-WASTED!

BE SURE TO EAT YOUR PEAS OFF YOUR KNIFE... IT'S FAR **EASIER** THAT WAY!

IT'S ALSO **BAD**! NO, I'LL EAT THEM THE PROPER WAY!
CHUCKLE! I'VE JUST REMEMBERED SOMETHING!

WHEN I WAS YOUR AGE, I USED TO PUT PEAS ON MY KNIFE, LIKE THIS...

...AND THEN BLOW THEM AT EVERYBODY, LIKE THIS! HO, HO!
HOWL! I GIVE UP! **DAD'S** FAR MORE LIKELY TO MAKE GUY BAD THAN I AM!
BLOW!
DAD! REALLY!

SOME TIME LATER...
AAAGH! GUY'S SMASHING EVERYTHING OFF THE TABLE!
HUH? HAS GUY BEEN BAD WHILE I WAS AWAY?

OH, BOY! THIS I'VE GOTTA SEE!

ALAS!
THERE HE GOES AGAIN! GUY'S **SMASH SHOT** IS THE BEST I'VE EVER SEEN!
HOWL! **THAT** KIND OF SMASH! MOUMFFF!
SMASH!

TERRY BAVE

WONDER WELLIES

REMEMBER WHAT HAPPENED EARLIER...

HEADMASTER! THIS BOY MADE ONE OF HIS WONDER WELLIES TIP SPAGHETTI, ICE-CREAM, GRAPES AND CHEESE ALL OVER ANOTHER BOY!

OOH, OOH! DISGRACEFUL! I SHALL CONFISCATE YOUR WELLIES, BOY! REMOVE THEM! NOW BACK TO YOUR CLASS!

I'LL GIVE HIM EXTRA HOMEWORK, HEADMASTER!

SHOVE!

EE! I'VE HEARD ABOUT WILLY'S WONDER WELLIES!

I WONDER IF THEY'LL WORK WONDERS FOR ME? I FEEL A BIT PECKISH, WELLIES! HOW ABOUT SOME OF THAT FOOD?

SHAKE!

WOW! THEY'RE OBEYING ME!

SPLOINK!

OKAY, WELLIES... THAT'S ENOUGH FOOD FOR MY LUNCH! STOP NOW... AND I'LL EAT! MMM!

SPLOINK!

Dave Follows.

BUT...

AARGH! I SAID STOP! STOP!

CRISPS

CRISPS

BREAK-TIME...

HEY, LOOK AT ALL THOSE SNACKS POURING OUT OF THE HEAD'S WINDOW! THEY MUST BE FOR US!

CRISPS

AAARGH! WILLY! TAKE BACK YOUR WELLIES! I NEVER WANT TO SEE THEM AGAIN!

HURL!

MUNCH!

CHOMP!

MUNCH!

MUNCH!

CHOMP!

SNIGGER! I WONDER WHAT'S EATING HIM?

MUMMY'S BOY

Jack Pott